The Write Stuff

500 Prompts to Jumpstart Your Writing

THE TACONIC WRITERS

PETER PAUPER PRESS, INC.
WHITE PLAINS, NEW YORK

PETER PAUPER PRESS
Fine Books and Gifts Since 1928

Our Company

In 1928, at the age of twenty-two, Peter Beilenson began printing books on a small press in the basement of his parents' home in Larchmont, New York. Peter—and later, his wife, Edna—sought to create fine books that sold at "prices even a pauper could afford."

Today, still family owned and operated, Peter Pauper Press continues to honor our founders' legacy—and our customers' expectations—of beauty, quality, and value.

Designed by Heather Zschock

Copyright © 2015
Peter Pauper Press, Inc.
202 Mamaroneck Avenue
White Plains, NY 10601
All rights reserved
ISBN 978-1-4413-1739-1
Printed in China
7 6 5 4 3 2 1

Visit us at www.peterpauper.com

The Write Stuff

500 Prompts to Jumpstart Your Writing

If you picked up this book, it means you have an interest in writing. Welcome to the clan! You may have heard it before, but it bears repeating: a writer writes! This book is filled with more than a year's worth of prompts, exercises, and thought-provoking tips designed with one purpose in mind: to keep you writing. The nine authors of this book, the Taconic Writers, have a collective total of more than a century of writing experience. All are professional writers of poetry, prose, or nonfiction. We've used many of the prompts and strategies you'll find in this book in our own writing or to help our fellow writers get unstuck.

About being stuck: It happens to almost every writer. Don't despair. Keep writing around the block and eventually the Muse will visit you again. That's another thing these exercises are good for. Sometimes a left turn into uncharted territory is just what's needed to jolt you into a fresh outlook or new creativity. The trick is to approach this journal without expectation or preconceived ideas. Let your imagination loose to ramble across these pages in your trademark scrawl. You can always edit or discard musings later. But if you don't put them to paper, they may well be lost forever. And that would be a terrible thing to do to an idea. If you run away with a prompt and want to take it further than the page allows, by all means keep going on paper or computer. The pocket inside the back cover is a handy place to store extra pieces of paper.

Keep writing. Write every day. Former U.S. Poet Laureate Ted Kooser writes a poem every single day. He probably writes a few terrible ones, but the amazing thing is, the more you write, the better you get at it. Flex your writing muscles and watch them grow strong. Most of all, have fun doing it. You don't know yet how good you are, or how good you will become.

Enjoy the journey!

Yours in ink,

The Taconic Writers

Great stories often begin with the arrival of a stranger. Have the stranger make a grand entrance, and then take it from there.

Explain why you want to write.

You've crashed a black tie event. How did you pull this off? Who do you meet, and how do you explain yourself? (Write in first, second, or third person; in your voice or another's.)

He knew if he walked under the arch of vines between the twin oaks at the forest's edge, the portal would lead him into a different realm. But he never would have guessed *this*.

You are on a whale-watching boat trip. When whales surface near your boat you suddenly realize you have the capacity to comprehend their language of whistles and croonings. You scuba dive to catch their every utterance, and surface to record their litany. What do they tell you?

An estranged friend from years ago contacts you to apologize for something you don't recall. Or vice versa. Do tell!

I left my heart in . . .

You are at the kitchen table. No one else is home. The morning sun spills through the window. Your hands wrap around a mug of steaming, fragrant coffee. What are you thinking about?

Your 21-year-old self suddenly appears across the table from you. What is he or she wearing? What advice or questions do you have for him or her? (You can answer this even if you are not yet 21.)

You are watching TV when a strange creature knocks at your door and asks to come in. You are pretty sure it is an extraterrestrial.

Write some dialogue set in the ladies' restroom of a society wedding.

A woman is helping her recently widowed friend in the garden. As she turns the petunia bed to prepare it for planting, she uncovers a severed hand.

You wander through a crowded antique shop stocked with all manner of bric-a-brac. Going up the stairs is precarious, for there's only a narrow footpath between piles of dusty books. One old tome catches your eye. You open it and are speechless, for the inscription inside is from none other than:

Be a music critic, making a case for or against a piece of music you find compelling.

Think of a word that has a funny sound to you. Write a poem or story with that word as the title. Don't think—write!

You've been hospitalized for an illness and are heavily medicated. An unfamiliar nurse enters your room and you're convinced she's an imposter planning to harm you. You will not take this lying down. You think of a stunning plan.

A friend's taste annoys you. Describe her joy over the choice item you eschew.

Your taste for _____ has changed. How?

Pro tip: Verbs

Strong verbs can be your best friends and can move your story along without cluttering it full of adverbs. Consider the following:

- He meandered into a bar.
- He scrambled into a bar.
- He strolled into a bar.

Not *all* verbs are your friends all the time, however. Sometimes it's impossible for them to do the job you've asked them to do. More exposition may be required to indicate the character's emotional state if you're using an abstract verb. You also run the risk of running into "purple prose" territory. Avoid using outlandish verbs just for the sake of it.

- He exploded into a bar.
- He jangled into a bar.

Summarize the plot of *War and Peace* or *Great Expectations* or *Moby Dick* in a short poem.

First meal or encounter with the parents of your love interest.

Billy Collins wrote: ". . . the poets are at their windows." Nothing is simpler. Stay there looking out until you see movement. Maybe just a car passing by. What kind? Color? How fast? Where do you think it's going? Who's driving? How do you feel about cars? About the state of the roads? Perhaps you will be moved to write by what is moving.

Be a butterfly and visit some flowers. Write about your flight, your landing, your sweet reward.

Lists imply writing, although some exceptional minds hold lists in their heads. For most of us, the words on paper help us remember what "to buy" or what "to do." Is there an item on your list, like mustard, that stirs your salivary glands, which in turn may heat up your imagination, so you can write some spicy lines?

Someone mistakes you for a very famous person. Go with it.

What did you do on your summer vacation? Sound familiar? This first of the school-year assignments was a writing prompt. It may jumpstart your writing now. Instead of the big picture, focus on a memorable moment or a snapshot, good or bad, funny or sad.

What's in your pocket/pocketbook? What do the objects you carry around reveal about you? Choose one and use it as a prompt to write about yourself, as though speaking to someone you just met. For example, consider your driver's license. How and when did you learn to drive? What state do you live in? How do you feel about your photo?

Talk techie. Technology is a catalyst for new words. Write a paragraph or poem using some of the words that have "loaded" into our language from the digital world. Words like hackerspace, bitcoin, pixel, applets, fiber network. Even more fun are old words with newer meanings: mouse, hardware, firewall, cookie, java, link, monitor, browser.

A conversation among zoo or barnyard animals. What might they be saying about the humans?

Pro tip: Dialogue

Words like "said" and "answered" become invisible to the reader. This is good! Use them as often as you like; they are the workhorses of your dialogue verbs. Avoid fussy verbs like, "he sneered," or "she chortled" when describing speech. Not only are these acts physically impossible, the emotion should be carried by the words of the dialogue themselves. If you need a supporting verb or adverb, consider rewriting the dialogue.

Set the scene and write the opening lines of dialogue for a play about a math teacher.

Write the dialogue for an argument between spouses. Write the 10,000th iteration of the same marital spat.

There was something not quite right about that carnival barker. Too late, I figured out what it was.

Airport arrival terminals are the site of many happy reunions. Write one.

Limerick
Challenge

If all you can do is write a sad poem
while you endeavor to build you a tome
'Twere better you did
stop writing and bid
Farewell _____

Write about a momentous event in understated black-and-white language, with no shades of gray.

Then relate the same event in hyperbolic, larger-than-life language.

Sour cherries, anchovy paste, pretzels, and sour cream are the signature ingredients of an old family recipe. Tell us about a scene associated with this or your own dish.

That tapping is not the steam heat, is it?

Pretend to be the moon. We are always writing about the moon from our earthly perspective; instead, write as though the moon were speaking to us on Earth!

Before he came home, the FedEx package arrived, addressed to him. She opened it.

He married WHO?

Begin a scene with this line of dialogue: "It's the principle of the thing!"

A well-groomed, middle-aged man follows a lithe younger woman as she strides across the sand of a luxury resort. He is stoop-shouldered as he addresses her. She responds without turning around. He stands straighter after he tips the cabana boy, who situates the woman on a chaise beneath an umbrella. The man then walks away, into the ocean. The sun glints off its surface. The man continues walking, then swimming, until he is barely a speck on the horizon. What is the relationship between the two?

Write a scene between them from a day during the previous week.

Captain Ahab walks into a bar . . .

A childhood fear.

You are locked into a dank dungeon. In the grim silence, you hear a tiny sound: grains of sand falling. Soon it becomes a clatter of gravel and mortar, and you are stunned to see a stone in the wall move inward toward you. What happens next?

Facing a perilous fall.

It's exactly the way my mother described it.

I sure picked the wrong day to give up _____! Why?

_____

_____

_____

Sometimes supporting characters are the juiciest. Choose a favorite supporting character from literature or film and write a plot line tailored to him or her.

_____

_____

_____

_____

_____

You are proposing marriage to your significant other and say the words "Will you . . . " when you suddenly and decisively change your mind.

_____

_____

_____

_____

You have been offered a free ride into space. Why would you accept or reject it?

Choose a piece of music that speaks to you, and set your own words to it. They can be poetry, lyrics, or prose.

A favorite author is sitting at the next table. Conversation ensues (with the narrator, or with the author's dining partner).

After designing, measuring, sawing, sanding, and assembling all parts with precision, your project is ready for its final coat of varnish. You set the piece outside to dry, take a quick break, then return to admire your masterpiece. A disaster. What's happened?

Funny, I wasn't expecting a package.

Write a paragraph of the letter that Tom penned to his college professor before committing himself to a psychiatric hospital.

Choose a random stranger and write a quick character sketch about him or her.

Remember the last time you got really angry. Tell about that from another's point of view.

Explain to a mafia boss why the pizza you delivered had a cardboard crust.

Write a children's story or poem about a fish.

Visiting the royal family.

You've just found a fancy silver spoon in the parking lot. What's the story?

I swear, I never saw it coming.

How would you have fared in medieval Europe?

A historical figure has just barged into your meeting or religious service. Who is it, and how do you and the others handle the interruption?

Got ink? Write about your tattoos or those of someone you know.

Alternative: observe a stranger's tattoos. Write about them.

A 16-year-old tech wizard accidentally hacks into the system of a secret government agency and learns something not even the president or CIA know. Now brilliant and powerful minds are onto her. How does she prevail?

What's the last thing you lost? Did you find it?

Describe a cupcake using every one of your senses. Sprinkle on some references to music, emotion, and calories.

Write the interior monologue of a person in the act of digging their own grave.

You find a love letter written to your grandmother by a movie star popular in her day. When you ask sweet little old Grandma about it, what she tells you is hard to believe.

Write a joke. Hint: you can switch up an old one. Can you think of some original twists on "Why did the chicken cross the road?" or "What is black and white and red all over?"

Mandy Farge grumbles and knits scarves when she's upset. The scarf she's been working on has become a shawl, then a bedspread, and it's still growing. What's bothering her?

A co-worker is spoiling for a fight. What's got her goat?

List the steps for getting back to normal.

Someone's just won big in Vegas, but their spouse isn't too happy. Describe the scene.

Skydiving or deep-sea diving? You can only choose one.

In your travels, you've encountered the last living dodo. What do you do?

What's better than the truth? The story! Take a favorite family story and embellish it to your heart's content.

You enter the funeral home and join the line of solemn mourners. Nodding to those near you as the line moves forward, you shake hands with several. As you near the casket, you realize you are at the memorial service for the wrong person. What next?

Your biography in ten words. Write six different versions.

You've invited several friends to a surprise birthday party. When the guest of honor arrives and everyone calls out, "Surprise!" she storms out. Describe the aftermath, or your conversation later with the birthday person.

Your new neighbor hangs laundry out to dry on a clothesline. Although she seems to live alone, she hangs out many articles of children's clothing. What do you imagine is going on next door?

Do you remember when you got the oldest item in your closet, and how you felt the first time you wore it?

Pro tip: Paring it down

Write as much—or as many—backstory (or stories) as you would like. These can stand alone, be worked into your main story, or take on lives of their own as springboards to other realms and new stories. Backstories can flesh out the history of characters and events. Or, once they've served their purpose to clear up your own mind about a character, they can be discarded.

A purple sun rises in the west one morning and makes its way east across a clear orange sky. Create a context.

Former queen of England Anne Boleyn was said to have been born with six fingers on one hand. Write about the way in which you or a fictional character is or feels different from other people.

Write about the most expensive gift you have ever received and how it came about.

Tell about the nicest gift you have ever given someone.

What is the very worst gift you have ever received? Who gave it to you and what was so terrible about it?

Children can't wait to write when asked to finish the phrase "I wish . . . ." Be a child again and write about your wishes.

Poke into plastic. Describe the assorted plastic containers in your cabinet. Do they resemble your life in any way, shape, or form? Are they—are you—mismatched, cracked, yellowed, tumbling off the shelf? Or are they—are you—neatly stacked, unstained, and absolutely useful?

Finish the phrase: "I wish I could play with language like…"

Tess Gallagher wrote a story, "The Lover of Horses," claiming that her grandfather was stolen by a horse. Have you ever been stolen by something? A deck of cards? Margaritas? Mystery books? Pen a few lines about your "gypsy necessity"—the urge to follow and surrender to the magnetic spell of something.

Your six-year-old son says: "I want a toy M16 dart machine gun." Write out the conversation you have with him.

Be an alchemist and turn an office memo into a poem.

Pro tip: Good guys are boring

There are few more fun writing experiences than giving life and voice to a juicy villain. Even your virtuous hero can—and often should—have a fatal flaw. The Seven Deadly Sins are wonderful engines for driving your characters.

Sometimes a particular poetic form is just what's needed to write, giving us a template with which to work, like the lines in a coloring book. Try the classic symmetry of a sonnet or the carousel ride of a villanelle or a plain quatrain. (Play with a rhyme scheme: abab, aabb, abba, or aaba.)

Dogs or cats? Toward which do you gravitate? People never tire of pet stories. What is yours?

You're an aspiring master villain, determined to rule the world. How will you accomplish this?

Starring in the final performance of a long theatrical run is a couple who in their private lives are long married. In their closing scene on stage, the actors, established as lovers, embrace. Suddenly one holds the other at arm's length, saying, then doing, what the playwright, audience, and partner could never have anticipated. What was said and done?

Breaking into a TV drama is an announcement that changes everything.

I had nailed it, having worked it through carefully. Then I asked for her opinion.

Flip the genders of characters in a well-known novel or play. How does the story change?

You've put it off for years, but circumstances convince you that it's now time to write your will.

The street sign read "Metered Parking Only."

The man's face was unusually smooth and pallid, but his manner quite the opposite, especially when his drink was slow to arrive.

Do a verbal selfie. An instant snapshot in words. Describe yourself and your surroundings in 30 words or less and say cheese.

You thought at first you were dreaming, but you have actually woken up on the rim of a crater on a distant planet. Fortunately, you find you can breathe, but now you must search for water. And you are hungry. You begin the long scramble down to the crater's interior, but you only go a few steps when you discover something even more unexpected.

Where's that giant bouquet of flowers headed? What kind of flowers are they?

Tell about your first pet.

A nun ducks into a confessional and emerges in a red dress and high heels. What's the story?

Pick the first sentence of a novel you like and write a totally different storyline about it.

They're trying to make me think I'm going crazy, but it isn't going to work.

"Lady Watson is not seeing any callers today."
"Oh, I think she'll see me."

A rare and deadly poison.

List five titles of the books you intend to write someday.

Your friend talks you into visiting a psychic. You expect an exotic gypsy behind a beaded curtain but what you get is a medium in a housecoat and orthopedic shoes. Who taps on the table and pays you a visit from the other side? And what are you being urged to do?

Imagine talking to a stranger who appears to be completely different from you. Who did you conjure and why? How did you start the conversation and what did you learn?

Make an unusual recipe figure prominently in a story.

Pro tip: Writing through writer's block

To overcome writer's block, consider the following. Are you stonewalled by a low stone wall, covered with lichen and moss, snaking through Robert Frost's farm? Or are you trapped between crumbling cinder-block highway abutments? Describing your inability to write can get you writing.

He knew conditions were unsafe for [diving, skiing, racing]. But there was no other choice.

Write your own obituary.

The boy is running away from home. Write a scene in which he is packing.

A man has a tattoo of two hands clasped around his neck. Why?

Marie Antoinette may never have said: "Let them eat cake." In *Confessions*, which was written when the queen was only 11 years old, author Jean-Jacques Rousseau attributed the statement to a smug noblewoman. Who else may have said those famous words? Put them into someone else's mouth in a context that renders an unexpected meaning.

Have fun with dialects. Try writing in a regional vernacular, or in the cadences of non-English speakers.

Write a haiku (three lines with syllables of 5-7-5) about a beloved childhood toy.

Stephen King cautions writers about "letting the monster out of the closet." Some things are more menacing if they remain out of sight, in the reader's imagination. Let the monster out of the closet, and then stuff him back in. How does your story change?

Communicate with someone, dead or alive, famous or not, and tell them how you wish they were here.

There have been many re-interpretations of Shakespeare's plays over the years—perhaps most famously reimagined by Baz Luhrmann's setting of *Romeo + Juliet* in a gritty urban environment. What would YOU do with Shakespeare?

Road trip: Write the story of a road. How did the road come into being? A cattle trail? A grand boulevard? Describe travelers on the road, from its very beginnings.

Pro tip: Solo or no?

Decide whether to create alone or collaborate. Share parts of your writings with others, or wait until finished and personally satisfied.

New neighbors move in next door and you invite them for coffee. After a congenial conversation, you make plans to see them again, but as they leave, one makes an obvious pass at you the other does not see. You close the door. What ensues?

Long car ride from the point of view of a child in the backseat.

Your lover has developed an allergy to you.

The black hole—what's in it?

The neighbor across the street has collected several rusting hulks of cars, which are an eyesore. You've asked him to remove them, and so has the local homeowner's group, yet he insists he's going to restore them to their former glory. You devise a plan to get rid of them and call the neighbors.

Where are you right now? Write from where you are, literally or figuratively.

Write about speed.

Write about a customer at a Korean nail salon from the manicurist's point of view.

You've gotten separated from the tour group. How? Why? Now what?

"If I told you once, I've told you a thousand times."

Think of two antithetical characters intolerant of one another. Now imagine they are paired on a treasure hunt or other endeavor with much at stake. Write the dialogue as they hash out their method of attack.

An embarrassing situation, but I wasn't embarrassed.

Go ekphrastic! Write a poem that comments upon another art form, such as a painting, a statue, a novel, or a film. W. H. Auden chose *Fall of Icarus* by Pieter Bruegel the Elder and wrote "Musee des Beaux Arts." Anne Sexton chose van Gogh's *Starry Night*.

Be inspired by a newspaper headline, but don't read the story. Write your own. Examples: "Road rage tailgater finds karma." "Sheep Storm France's Louvre."

Your realtor asks you to meet her/him at the fixer-upper. You arrive early and wait, but then decide to go in. It's dark and smells musty, but you climb the stairs to the dim landing, where a patch of sun illuminates something disturbing. You gasp. What is it?

"I drew a breath, set my teeth, gripped the starting lever with both hands, and went off with a thud." (H. G. Wells, *The Time Machine*) Where will you go from here?

Describe a bus terminal in the wee hours of a winter morning.

Add new lines to old familiar lines:
- There was a man from Timbuktu . . .
- Candy is dandy but liquor is quicker . . .
- Now is the time for all good men (women) to . . .
- I could've been a contender . . .

Limerick Challenge

There was a young scribbler of notes
Who got many an old writer's goats;
for he plagiarized much;
now the moral is such
when you're young do not_____

The dry cleaner handed him the freshly cleaned, wrapped formal suit. He hailed a taxi to the bus terminal, anticipating the evening wedding. Underway, relaxed, he undid the wrap in order to place the suit in his travel bag. One glance told him it was not his.

Brainstorm about bridges. Write a short story, brief memoir, or essay based on one of your ideas. Here are some starters:

- We used to meet under the old covered bridge . . .
- He was afraid of bridges, so he . . .
- The scariest or most impressive bridge I ever crossed . . .
- The bridge between the past and the future . . .

Hiring your mother.

Though she couldn't pay the rent, she had a solution.

Spiders everywhere!

Penelope's Labrador retriever, a constant companion by her wheelchair, died this morning. Knowing his passing was imminent, she'd taken up her diary and written to him, the closest friend she'd ever known.

Pro tip: Decide on writing pace

Time deadline or open-ended? Don't rush; speed kills. But sometimes writing quickly bypasses the inner critic overthinking things.

You are being awarded an honorary degree from a university. What for?

Compose a poem about ears. Or toes. Or a nose. Poet Edmond Rostand wrote an entire play based on an overly large nose (*Cyrano de Bergerac*).

Feeling lonely.

No . . . I couldn't settle for just one.

Use something about your last doctor's visit to spark a paragraph. A character in the waiting room? Earrings the nurse was wearing? Something the doctor said? Include details and write it as fast as you can. You can always fix it later. But write it.

The guardian angel who watches over you is making a report on your last ten years. What will the angel say?

Pro tip: No sacred cows

Chances are, if that line, phrase, or paragraph is bothering you, it will bother your reader as well. Delete it or rewrite it.

You are on an elevator. A suspicious character gets on. A floor later, the elevator breaks down. You are stuck for many hours.

Same scenario with an unnervingly attractive person.

Plead for clemency for a defendant you know is guilty.

If you're an only child, invent siblings. If you have siblings, imagine life as an only child.

Al Capone and Buddha walk into a bar together. Al Capone says, "I'm buying."

The worst magic act in the world.

Write about something extremely sensual: a delicious meal, a beautiful vista, a sexual experience—without using a single adjective.

An influential citizen attempts to persuade the editor of the hometown newspaper to endorse a very unpopular position or candidate.

Five beautiful American women and an Irish priest spend a week together in an apartment in Paris. Fill in all the blanks.

Describe a character's favorite garment, and how it defines him or her.

Throw together some oddball adjectives and nouns. Why is purple prose purple? What makes a bad joke "cheesy?" How can these stock phrases be improved?

Pick the topic you know least about: a) wrestling an alligator, b) the theory of relativity, or c) head wounds. Now wing it. Write with feigned confidence. Use your imagination and as many invented terms and facts as you need.

At the reading of her parents' will, Mindy is shocked to find out that she was adopted. What are the circumstances of her birth and why was it kept secret until now?

Sometimes children grow up with affectionate but limiting labels (e.g., the good-looking one, the smart one, the funny one, the shy one, or the baby). Write about an attractive multitalented person who still hasn't learned to trust his whole arsenal of gifts enough to use them. A fictional character or someone you know? Oh? Could that be you?

Just before the curtain rises on a popular British farce, the usher guides someone to an already-occupied seat in the theatre. Both tickets are identical. An argument ensues. It seems everyone in the house gets into the act. It's a farce within a farce. Write it.

Consider the periodic table of the elements. Write characters based on the commonly accepted perceptions of elemental properties. Try iron, gold, mercury. Or maybe you know some noble gases? Is someone you know radioactive?

If you could have a face-to-face encounter with a mythical creature, which would it be? Describe the encounter.

A Halloween costume in the worst possible taste.

Think of someone you knew long ago but have lost touch with, and write a character sketch of what they might be like now.

Step inside a board game and write the story of Mouse Trap, Monopoly, or Candy Land—or your own favorite.

A rich man decides to give away all his money. Describe his last day with funds, and his first day without.

Chopping onions.

Choose a piece of abstract art and write a narrative about it.

Pick an animal. Dress it in clothes and put it in a setting. For example, a hippo in a track suit at a PTA meeting. An alligator in tie-dye at a ballpark. A lizard in Dior at the Four Seasons. Write an interior monologue or a vignette based on this character.

Describe an overpowering smell and what it brings to mind.

Write a flirtatious dialogue.

They say even "empty space" fizzes with energy. If empty, follow the fizz. Start writing from exactly where you are. Choose a physical prompt from your environment, or go with the first thought that comes into your head.

Write a sermon.

Pro tip: Place as character

Read about locales at home and abroad. They add color.

She's got no talent—none. So how did this happen?

A timed scribble. Set a timer for three minutes and write quickly, ignoring legibility or style. Never lift your pen. The physical act of writing words on paper, more so than typing them, stimulates our brain. A seedling idea may emerge. Look for a crocus poking up out of the debris.

There is a movie that keeps running through your head. Imagine yourself in the role of a character: hero, villain, or wallflower. How would you change the movie?

Tell the blank page about how your first sexual experience began, real or imagined.

A large, celebrity-studded group at a five-star restaurant is becoming increasingly unruly. What does the maître d' do?

An 80-year-old wakes up one morning and realizes that something has to change.

An 18-year-old wakes up one morning and realizes that something has to change.

Peruse and have fun with weather jargon. Combine terms such as polar vortex, popcorn convection, and cumulus congestus in a prose poem.

Tell a five-year-old how to tie a bow.

Flex your punny bone by writing a paragraph using excruciatingly bad puns.

If you know a second language, even just a few words or phrases, try writing macaronic verse, mixing two or more languages. Such poetry is often funny. Take a look at Brian Cleary's book, *Rainbow Soup: Adventures in Poetry*.

"How do I love thee? Let me count the ways." Elizabeth Barrett Browning shares the lyrical ways she loves her beloved. What are your ways? Declare, in your own way, your own love—for a person, or a place, or a thing.

Hippocrates theorized four "humors," or personality types. Write the same scene from the point of view of each: choleric, melancholic, sanguine, and phlegmatic. Explore other psychological theories and use them to experiment with characters.

Where do you long to be? Behind the scenes or center stage?

Confess. Ever gotten away with something you knew was wrong? Tell all.

Most writers are voyeurs. Jot down snatches of conversation overheard in restaurants or other public spaces. Build your story around these.

Having just completed his final in-air training with his instructor, he got a thumbs-up to take control of the Piper Cub for his first solo flight. Airborne for less than five minutes, the engine sputtered, then failed. There was only one thing he could do.

A doctor's dilemma.

You notice an envelope slipped halfway under your door. What's in it, and what does this mean?

Weigh the pros and cons of adopting an infant from another country.

Visualize your dream home. Describe it.

A nephew has given you an iguana for a present and asks you to help him write an essay entitled "Why the iguana is the most beautiful creature in the world."

You plan to eat at a remote inn, and when you arrive the door is locked. You knock and are confronted by a tall man with a glass eye. He tells you the inn is closed, but since you have driven so far, he will serve you. Dinner is slow in coming, and while you wait, you hear screams upstairs and observe menacing men passing through the dining room. You look out the window and your car is missing.

Write a sentence that goes on for all seven lines below. Use as little punctuation as possible.

You've caught a respected person in a very compromising situation. What's going on?

A botanist visits Washington, D.C., in April to view its famous cherry blossoms. Just before sunrise, she walks the path of trees when she is shocked to observe the clouds of pink flowers turn blood red.

Think about how to crack the passwords on the computer of a dear friend, or that of a bitter rival. What is it you need to access, and why?

The owner of a small-time circus discovers something weird and horrifying happening to the performers and animals. What's going on?

A small town hero's homecoming. What did he/she do, and how is it being celebrated?

Pro tip: No mercenaries

Try not to write to a specific audience. Your audience will find you.

"It was a dark and stormy night." Write this sentence ten different ways.

Write an "in between" poem. In between the sheets . . . In between relationships . . . In between classes . . .

Your favorite literary character sets up an "Ask Me Anything" blog. Go for it!
Write your questions and the character's answers.

What are you looking for as you wander through the maze of stalls at the flea market?

Write a letter to your best friend telling why you are concerned for his safety.

Invent a superhero (or heroine) and supply some brand-new superperson powers and gadgets.

Make up fresh lyrics for an old tune, e.g., "Happy Birthday to You."

Think of a person with an annoying trait. Now write a conversation between that person and a character who's fallen in love with them at first sight and finds that trait adorable.

Accidental poetry! Most writers are book lovers. Stacks of books everywhere? String the titles on the spines together to create a poem. Although you can throw out any that don't "work," it's more fun to try to fit everything together, no matter how incongruous. The results will surprise you.

"Of all the gin joints in all the world, she walks into mine." Write about a strange coincidence, and what transpires.

Two dogs on leashes snarl and lunge at each other as their owners try to pull them apart. After a ruckus, the canines are separated. What do the owners say to each other?

Pro tip: The perspective of distance

Let your first working draft sit for a while. Then re-read it.

A change in the weather can change the whole tenor of a story. Imagine the identical incident taking place in a snowstorm, sunshine, or on a foggy morning.

Pretend to be a fortune-teller. Describe your clientele, and their fortunes, on an average day.

Put yourself or your character in a *Sophie's Choice* situation. Write your way out of it.

There is a house in your neighborhood which has always intrigued you. Did someone odd live there? Did something haunting occur there? Do tell.

On a flight to visit a friend, a passenger attempts to hijack your plane. You arrive safely and tell the friend what happened.

Think of a poem or a lyric you especially like, pick out a phrase or a line, and incorporate it into a narrative scene.

Driving at night, you find yourself lost in a bad part of town. You pull into an alley in order to turn around, and see several people staring at you. You put your car in reverse, but it stalls. The people approach your vehicle. Your heart thumps with fear. Next . . .

He awoke to find she was not there. He went to the kitchen, where coffee was brewing and bread was toasting, to find a note on her empty plate. "It's been wonderful, Rick, but it's time. I'm leaving you."

The sky has long intrigued you. What special vista has lingered in your memory: a cloud formation, a plane towing an advertising banner, a blazing sunset?

Glancing out your apartment window, you see someone inside a Dumpster, rifling through its contents. They pause and hold something up. Is it a porcelain figurine? A torn envelope? A lottery ticket? The person climbs out of the Dumpster, gingerly carrying the object. Curious, you tear down the stairs and follow them. Where does the person lead you, and what does it reveal about the significance of the object?

Take or recall a family picture. Describe it from another family member's point of view.

What are the triumphs of your body? Its defeats?

Write a seasonings poem, using saffron, rosemary, thyme, pepper, sage, oregano, parsley, curry, or any other combination that causes you to salivate.

Satan's cell phone. Or Jesus's.

Limerick
Challenge

I'm missing a ruffian to round out my tale
but I am determined that I will not fail
so I'll search in my past
for a _____ to cast
and fit him as _____

Once I purchased what I thought was the perfect souvenir from Jamestown, Virginia. This historic area is known for making glass, and while there, I was mesmerized by artisans demonstrating glassblowing. I bought a spring-green glass vase with a scalloped rim, ideal for daffodils. Write about an object that captured a place for you.

Write a playground poem. Have your way with the seesaw, slide, or jungle gym.

Psychologists know we are drawn to repetition. We feel more disposed toward things we encounter again and again. Write a poem that repeats a line. For a challenge, try a rondeau, composed of 15 lines, eight to ten syllables each, divided into stanzas: a quintet, a quatrain, and a sestet. The refrain consists of the first few words or the entire first line of the first stanza, and recurs as the last line of both the second and third stanzas. Two rhymes guide the music of the rondeau; its rhyme scheme is as follows (R representing the refrain): aabba aabR aabbaR.

Harry lost the biggest sale of his career to Dan, a competitor. A million-dollar contract. They had for years been close friends, and Harry had learned the tricks of the trade from him. But when Harry reached for his office phone, Dan, out of character, spoke to him with words that made the wound deeper still.

Pick an incident that occurred when you were learning to drive. Remember as many details as you can.

Oh, no—not that song. Before you change the station, think about the incident that made you hate that song. Write about the incident. Change the ending.

Novel Writing 101

Why do you want to write a novel? Give three reasons.

Come up with an idea for the novel. You have a story somewhere in the back of your head? Sketch it.

Brainstorm to develop a plot: write down ideas without regard to order. Decide what ideas to include and what to leave out.

Decide whether to outline the novel in detail before beginning, or to wing it as you go along. If the former, write an outline of the plot and subplots. If the latter, start writing.

Make up names that bring to your mind certain characters that feature in your story, then write brief biographies of your principal characters.

Write a first sentence to your novel from several points of view.

Write an ending sentence of your novel. Or several possibilities.

Make a list of items you need to research to make your novel plausible.

Draw a timeline, with dates for completing the different parts of the novel.

Analyze the last novel you have read, outlining the main plot, major subplots, point of view, and themes.

Limerick
Challenge

My mind has the pieces that make a novel,
but I am not sure that they all hang too well;
they're lacking the glue
that'd make them come true
in _____

Describe a pair of jeans in detail, as though you were the designer, touting form, function, and fit.

_____

_____

_____

_____

Write the tasting notes for an astoundingly bad wine.

_____

_____

_____

_____

Your last hundred dollars.

_____

_____

_____

Defend your recent purchase of an extravagant and out-of-character item.

Ancient oceanic peoples navigated the Pacific Ocean and colonized Hawaii, Easter Island, and other lands in outrigger canoes. What did they do to pass the time on those long voyages? What did they carry?

Your mother finds ways to make mountains out of molehills.

Pro tip: Pruning

If words don't add anything to the piece, delete them. "When in doubt, leave it out."

Write some journal entries by a fiendishly obsessed collector, or a stalker. Explore the objects of their obsessions, and their actions to acquire them.

They both knew he might be riding (driving, flying) into certain death. Then, she pressed something into his hand.

That faux drumming that you do: finger thumps or pencil whacks. Speak the rhythm or tune into verse.

What happens in Vegas stays in Vegas. Except when it doesn't.

Write six lines of dialogue in which two characters completely misunderstand almost everything the other says.

Snow White woke up with a kiss and married the prince 22 years ago. What does her life look like after "happily ever after"?

Yeah, he was what my dad used to call "a heavy hitter."

Spend an hour in a coffee shop and write about the people's comings and goings.

Write an acceptance speech for your screenwriting Oscar. Make it heartfelt and humble. Begin it with a comment that shows your surprise at winning. Then throw in the works.

Pro tip: *What do they want?*

Find the motivation—the raison d'être—of supporting characters.

Describe the interior of a cave where someone is living.

Write a poem about how to write a poem.

There's a start-up business emerging just about every day. And here you stand idle with an inventive idea that can move the world.

Design a ten-question reader's quiz. Use sincere questions or make it spoofier than spoof.

Write a *Saturday Night Live* sketch.

You are visiting friends when their six-year-old tells a very dirty joke he heard at school.

There's "business"—an activity carried out in the course of a story that doesn't necessarily move it along—and then there's "action"—which has the potential to change everything. Write about an everyday act (washing the dishes, taking out the trash) in both modes. How does your story change?

Pro tip: The theme

Develop a central theme—from personal experience or invented.

You've boarded your aircraft and settled in for a long flight when a bubbly blonde in a purple minidress plops into the seat next to you. "Ever hear the saying 'Blondes have more fun'?" she asks. "Well, lemme tell ya something . . . "

_____

_____

_____

_____

Maps can be great story springboards. Choose a location at random—preferably one about which you know nothing—and feature it in a snippet.

_____

_____

_____

_____

_____

_____

Write about an unusual form of transportation as experienced by a glamorous movie star, a straitlaced minister, or a convicted criminal.

The general must explain to the head of state why the mission has failed.

Henry's chances are 50/50; the payoff would be huge. How can he cling to his firm belief in Murphy's Law?

The ghost you saw.

The ghost you wish you saw.

Remember a storybook or fairy tale you loved as a child. Did you read it for comfort during a sad time or illness, or because you liked a scary adventure? Write about why it appealed to you.

Riding a roller coaster.

Someone backs out of the garage without noticing that their spouse's car is in the way, damaging both vehicles. Write the couple's ensuing conversation.

Pro tip: What if?

Play "What If?" Imagine. No subject or character or event is out of bounds.

You discover that your boss has falsified elements of his résumé. How do you handle this? Can you use this to your advantage?

_____

_____

_____

_____

_____

Is there something that frustrates or angers you so much that you want to scream or at least grit your teeth? Write a scene about someone who feels this way but then does something unexpected.

_____

_____

_____

_____

_____

_____

You have just purchased a new boat, larger than your last, and are learning how to handle it. You've invited several friends along for the first run. All are having fun when someone says, "Look at those black thunderclouds!" and you turn to see an ominous storm between you and the shore.

She spoke ever so quietly. Just one word. And he knew.

You have won a $25 million lottery. Plan what you will do tomorrow.

_____

_____

_____

_____

Twist the tongue twisters. Read John Hollander's "Marine Tongue Twister." Each verse ends with a variation on "She sells seashells by the seashore." ("She sells she-shells by the seashore. She shells seashells by the seashore," etc.) Create a poem by twisting the words: "A proper copper coffee pot" or "Betty Botter bought a bit of butter" or "Six sheep sip thick shakes" or your own original.

_____

_____

_____

_____

A younger sibling wins an athletic championship, scholastic competition, chess match, or some such, succeeding at something an older sibling has long desired but has failed to achieve. Describe the family dinner that night.

_____

_____

_____

_____

Create a dystopian future world. Populate it with strange contraptions, characters, and cultural conventions. Would a person of today be able to access this world? How?

What did not come in yesterday's mail?

Jeffrey pilots a single-wing, single prop, eight-seat plane on short commercial hops. Today is a day like any other, until one of the passengers turns out to be someone Jeffrey hoped he'd never see again.

Pro tip: Getting ideas

To generate ideas, reflect on pain, sorrow, loss, tragedy, or people you love, despise, envy, or admire.

You have a minor fender bender when the elderly woman driving the other car emerges with a pistol pointed at you.

Not angry, enraged.

You're a reporter on the courthouse steps. The blockbuster verdict has just been delivered. Get the star witness to make a statement.

Now get one of the jurors to talk.

Tear a collection of glossy images from magazines and keep a box of them. Choose one and integrate it into a scene.

Stop badgering me!

Your favorite color used to be _____.

What are ten things you want to be sure to experience within your lifetime?

Do you know who's calling before the phone rings? Do watches stop the moment you strap them on your wrist? Explore your sixth sense, or one you'd like to have.

Which of your dreams resonates with you? Do you have a recurring dream or recurring theme? Are your dreams travelogues, adventures, or disconnected images? Would you like to rewrite the ending of one or more?

The planet upon which you were born.

Write three classified ads, one for the "help wanted" section to find someone who can make sense of it all, another to sell something completely useless, and the third to rent an apartment with a spectacular view of an imaginary landscape.

Modernize the story (or a scene) of *Goldilocks* using people instead of bears.

Write about an electrical appliance. Make it sexy.

You live in a boardinghouse with three other people. Describe them.

Pro tip: Thrift shop your own writing.

Go through your false starts and discarded first drafts. Just because you had to kill a first paragraph or a line of poetry doesn't mean it had no value. Take a yellow highlighter and mark amusing phrases, interesting images, and seedling ideas that are worth resuscitating.

Martin never dreamed it could happen. And then it did. So, how will he deal with it?

_____

_____

_____

_____

What sense or body part could you live without? How would you adapt?

_____

_____

_____

_____

At last, you forgot his birthday.

_____

_____

_____

They want you at the police station. Why?

_____

_____

_____

_____

A male friend with whom you are having lunch calls your attention to his bright red nail polish and asks you to guess why he is wearing it.

_____

_____

_____

_____

A new business has opened up on Main Street. What is it, and how does it change the neighborhood?

_____

_____

_____

_____

_____

A pleasant woodland path suddenly turns ominous. What's happening?

Everyday life has its own beats and rhythms. Growing up around rotary phones, I can remember the rhythmic "click-click" as my mother dialed a number late at night. Take note as you go through your day: of traffic, footsteps, ice cubes tinkling in a glass. Write a poem in one of the tempos, or write about your observations.

She was a creature of habit—kind of like her dog. Move his food bowl from its usual place in the corner of the kitchen and he won't eat.

You are in your neighbor's living room petting their dog when suddenly . . .

The obituary is horribly inaccurate and amounts to libel.

You realize that you are cooking without a recipe.

After divorcing the one-time love of your life a year ago, he or she has just turned up at your door.

There's something odd about the paintings at the museum. They appear in different positions from one day to the next.

Some of the most well-known authors blend two or more genres: Philip K. Dick (sci-fi/detective/noir), Cormac McCarthy (western/horror). Mash up two genres and see what you get.

Write about a car you loved or hated.

The old-age home for retired spies and double agents.

A botched bank robbery.

Pro tip: The medium and the message

If you're accustomed to keyboarding, try a yellow legal pad and a sharp pencil.
How does the flow of your writing change? Change your medium, change your mind.

Think of the nearest airport to your house, even if it's not a commercial airport.
What's going on there right now?

Write a poem playing with a series of homonyms (words that look and/or sound like
another word with a different meaning). Some examples:
  • Iron: a metal; a device to press materials flat
  • Mole: raised mark on the skin; animal underground
  • Days: more than one day; Daze: to bewilder
  • Knead: to work bread dough; Need: must have

You, a human being, have been dropped into a cartoon à la *Who Framed Roger Rabbit*.

Go to a hardware or paint store and grab some paint chips. Describe something using the color names of one or more of the chips.

Describe your father without using any adjectives.

Of course you would never harm anyone. Not even the rat who cheated on you, or the relative who tried to swindle you out of your inheritance. But heightened emotion can boost creativity. Dream up sneaky, oddball ways to get even with someone and use them in a story. Who knows—it could be just the ticket to successful publication. Now that revenge would be sweet.

Once again, you are flying in a dream. How do you do it?

Not long ago you went someplace and remember part of the journey in exquisite detail. What happened?

It is the year 2084. After the information explosion came the bio explosion. You're alive, but composed (mostly) of replacement parts. And your pet is a curated composite of several different animals. Compare him to your first "unaltered" puppy.

A newcomer to your office has a surprising talent.

Pro tip: Relax

Blank Page Syndrome is akin to White Coat Syndrome; it's mostly temporary. If staring at a blank page makes you sweat, go for a walk with paper and pen in your pocket.

How would you end *Gone with the Wind* differently?

Mix it up. Some of the best writing comes from putting two things together that ordinarily don't go together. Put the duchess in the trailer park. Have the janitor save the opera on opening night.

You (or your character) are spelunking without a guide. You follow a well-worn path through a series of large caverns and passages until you come to a magnificent stalagmite-studded hall. But your flashlight dims; you must head back *now*. You turn to find that your path was not the only way. You cannot distinguish between the two dark tunnels before you. Write your way out.

List the soundtrack for your current project. There are no wrong answers.

In the basement of a public library, you discover…

Time goes so fast now.

Tell your spouse's parents why you are leaving him (her) after six months of marriage.

It's a wrong number, but the caller sounds interesting. Play along.

Take a setting and really dig into it. Describe it down to the smallest detail. Try to use all the senses.

That wallflower over there has been studying the way you dance with Charlie.

Write the same confession as heard by the local bartender and the parish priest. What advice does each one give?

Again you're being told to "get over it."

The pills are having a very strange and unexpected side effect. It appears to be permanent. What's the story?

An acquaintance has died. You volunteer to clean out her attic. You're shocked at what you find. Do you keep the secret, or tell all?

A sporty blue convertible zips down the parkway, passing other cars. A silver-haired man drives. A woman is beside him; her body appears young, but her face is hidden by a floppy hat. What happens next?

Anthony is paid an eight-figure salary—and for what?

Tell the story (or a scene) of *Pinocchio* in the first person with Pinocchio as narrator.

A character has stopped speaking to you. Ask her to join you for a walk.

Laura can no longer put up with the mess he makes.

A famous portrait begins speaking. Who is it, and what is it saying?

Jane is superstitious. She has lucky numbers, owns a pair of lucky socks, and deciphers meaning from random events. Describe her day, starting with the song that woke her this morning on her radio.

Pro tip: Canoodling with characters

Have fun with character descriptions: physical, emotional, behavioral, sartorial, sloppy, or stylish habits. Do they speak in a vernacular? What's in their closets? You can always delete extraneous detail once you've gotten to know your characters better.

Overcoming shyness.

Where do all those unmatched socks go?

"No one's fault," I heard myself say.

Write the instructions for a common task like washing the car. Make them funny.

The DNA results are obviously wrong.

Describe the end of a long, exhausting journey. Where have you arrived?

The best laugh you ever had.

The best laugh you ever had, but no one else was laughing.

The one person who made such a moving impression on you years ago at college has contacted you via handwritten letter.

Your hand on the combination lock, you are waiting to remember.

He waits at the airport baggage claim for his portfolio of samples. But it's a no-show—and his long-awaited interview with six execs is scheduled at headquarters minutes from now. What's next?

You're approaching a popular beach on a sunny day, and as you clamber over the dunes toward the surf, you see not a single person along the entire shore. You feel a frisson of terror. Where is everyone? What happens? What do you do?

As she scooped caviar with an ivory spoon, she scoffed at the idea that they'd ever catch her. Until one of her companions pointed toward the door.

Write a poem concerning the absence of something. Consider the absence as a positive.

You are six. You run away from home. Your mother finds you at your best friend's. Describe the scene in the car driving home.

Choose a character who dies in the course of the novel. Now imagine how the story would have turned out had that character lived.

You've discovered a secret stash. Whose is it? What is it? What do you do with it?

Well, do you tell them? Or don't you? It's been haunting you for years.

Everyone's got a perspective. Write the hare. Then write the hawk.

Sometimes we are tongue-tied when we self-censor. Think of the blank page as representing your inhibitions, staring up at you, daring you. What do you really want to write?

Explain to your significant other why there is vomit in the backseat of the car.

She makes George an offer she feels he can't refuse. Yet he does.

Try Skeltonic verse, named after John Skelton (1460–1529). It uses fast and frequent rhyming and very short lines. Choose a subject (rain) and let the rhymes carry you (the rain in Spain stays mainly on the plain) until you find that the rhyme is exhausted and you move on to another one (but when the rain is done, the sun has lots of fun).

You've just discovered several photos on your camera you know you didn't take. Who took them? What are they of?

Serving time in prison for a crime he did not commit, the mostly illiterate inmate sat on his cot with paper and pencil and composed a poem to Daisy Fay, the only girl he'd ever wanted to marry.

Invent a cliché.

You return to an old haunt of your youth. What do you find there? How has it changed?

Use the word "reflection" literally as a device or figuratively as a theme, and write quickly for one minute.

What would you write with a fountain pen filled with liquid gold ink? Write a poem to evoke the feeling of those glowing words. Prose poem, haiku, sonnet—as you see fit.

Write about the day you first felt like an adult.

Matilde must leave home tonight but can't decide whether she should elope with John or take the next boat to America alone. She talks it over with herself while packing, carefully choosing the items that will fit in her small suitcase. Write the monologue.

Tell your fiancé that you have an illegitimate child.

You enter the art museum after a robbery and are shocked to find a number of master-pieces have been cut from their frames. What would you say to the thieves and/or the detectives on the case?

Her father's Remington typewriter still sat on a rolling table in her room. He was a newspaper columnist who'd ground out daily commentaries. Now his machine was idle. Without knowing why, she took a sheet of paper from her printer and rolled it into the platen. Her fingers on the keys, she typed these words:

When writing fiction, develop a starting chronological outline of characters and events.

Today's high-level job interview rolled along remarkably well. Until you opened your mouth once too often.

Visit a cemetery—the older, the better. Write a biographical sketch or two based on headstones you find. Or start a family saga if you stumble upon a family tomb or mausoleum.

Write four rhyming lines celebrating what you had for lunch today.

Write a haiku (three lines: 5-7-5 syllables per line) about an Oriental rug.

Finish the micro-story that includes this line of dialogue: "I have traveled a long way from where I began."

On the first day just name it. _____

On the next day write one sentence about it.

Add a sentence on each subsequent day for the next week.

Eating a hot dog.

Write about getting lost.

Your tiny dog makes a little sound—"Ow, ow, ow"—when she wants to go out.
But yesterday it almost sounded like, "I love you." Today you think she may have said,
"Those pants make you look fat." What's going on?

Limerick
Challenge

If the great novel you would compose
here is what I'd first propose
go fly a kite
quite late at night
and all the next morning _____

"The Egyptian god Ra sprang to life with a word already in his mouth. Ra shouted that first word, over and over, and those shouts rose in molten mass up and up and spewed forth in a fiery explosion. In his voice lay all creation."

—Donna Jo Napoli, "Treasury of Egyptian Mythology," *National Geographic*, 2013

Wow. The power of words. What word(s) would you choose to shout?

Explain to the child why it's OK to go in the water.

While visiting a foreign city, you encounter a state or religious leader whose views you strongly disagree with. Describe the meeting.

Most of the phone message was cut off. The only part you hear is, "You know I wouldn't ask you if there was any other way."

Dyspeptic desperado and his pet macaw on the lam.

I've kept that photograph for a year now—even had it framed. It sits on the night table beside my bed. Am I deranged?

A film crew stops you on the street and says you will win $5,000 if you name all the U.S. presidents in order. You are allowed one phone call for help. You begin confidently: "Washington, Adams, Jefferson, Madison," when your mind goes blank. Who do you call and what happens?

Write a mathematical poem, celebrating the beauty of math or explaining a topic in a lyrical form using math terms.

He's racing through the store, basket in hand, to stock up before the storm strikes. But the only thing left on the shelves is _____ and he needs _____.

Your boss has invited you to his home for dinner and you want to make a good impression. You enjoy the conversation and keep it politically correct—until he shows you his prized collection, which shocks you. What is it and why is it disturbing?

Examine an object as though you were going to draw it. Shape. Size. Heft. Color. Then try to honor it with an ode. Pablo Neruda liked odes: "Ode to an Artichoke," "Ode to My Socks," "Ode to a Large Tuna in the Market." He made the ordinary extraordinary. Pick an object that intrigues you. Perhaps a single drop of rain.

Select a passage from a well-known work. Edit it. If it's full of adjectives, pare it down. If it's spare, juice it up.

You've been called for an interview for which you have thoroughly prepared. You enter the office, ready to dazzle. But the interviewer behind the desk is the father of a former love, and that relationship ended badly. What do you say first?

Choose a mundane scenario: dining at a restaurant, riding the bus, etc. Write a paragraph describing it in three different genres.

"Age has nothing to do with me." Do you agree? Write about an age issue that concerns you, like turning 18 or 40, or being a woman or man "of a certain age."

You are canoeing through a tunnel of mangrove trees under a full moon. What do you find when you emerge on the other side?

The first hometown sight you would show a Martian, and how you would explain its significance.

Write about the wind as if it was something new.

Write about betrayal.

You find an airplane ticket to Bali in your husband's desk.

Remember Hal in the movie *2001: A Space Odyssey*? What would your computer like to say to you?

Write a poem that follows the meter and placement of parts of speech from a famous poem or a poem you particularly like.

You drop your child off at school one morning. That evening, the school calls to ask why your child was absent that day.

Write about the place you live in now. Or a childhood home. "Walk" through the rooms or around the block. What do you see, hear, and smell? An orange shag rug? A sprinkler misting a manicured lawn? The earthen odor of a cobwebbed-filled basement? A pink-tiled bathroom? Jot down snippets, then try to sew them together.

Pro tip: Change it up

If you have been working in the same environment (same location, same time of day, same writing medium, etc.), change it up! Try something different as an experiment.

Write a short dialogue or scene about two strangers sharing an overnight train compartment.

You've recently met a couple who've asked you to join them at their vacation home for a week. You gladly accept; however, upon arrival you see it is not the cozy little cottage you envisioned, but a screenless shack rife with insects. To make matters worse, the bathroom is an outhouse. How do you escape?

Your significant other has asked you why you don't want to talk in the morning.

You are a civilian guest of NASA on a space mission. Why were you chosen?

Select a well-known Bible story or myth. Rewrite it, setting it in modern times.

Your friend asks your expertise in determining the soundness of a house he hopes to buy. As you join him there, you see it is an attractive buy, but you experience a shiver of apprehension upon entering. How do you mention your premonition of impending doom to your friend?

You come inside after your garage sale, gleefully counting your money, when you look into the space where something of value is missing. What have you sold that you regret?

With international turmoil commanding the pages of her newspaper, she thought, "Here we go again . . . as if there is anything I can do about it." Then it came to her.

A baby pops a slice of lemon in her mouth. Describe what happens from the point of view of the father.

A detective is asking you how you got that black eye.

A web search has turned up some unexpected and disturbing results.

Tell Mrs. Smith's third-grade class what you do for a living.

It's Ladies' Night at the Roach Motel Honky-Tonk. What are the lady bugs up to?

Include this in a narrative: "I'm sorry," she said. "No second chances."

The restaurant server prompts by asking, "May I start you with a drink?" Drinks, in turn, may be prompts for us. What do you normally order? Why? What did you drink as a child? Kool-Aid? Do certain drinks bubble with memories? Did you ever have champagne at the Ritz in Paris? What is the most exotic beverage you've ever sampled?

Compose a haiku (three lines with syllables of 5-7-5) about a pet peeve.

Write the biography of a one-dollar bill.

It is Veteran's Day and a commentator on your car radio mentions we should thank those who have served, regardless of our feelings about war. There's a car in the parking lot in front of you; its license plate frame announces a veteran. You walk up to the window to speak to him/her. Describe the conversation.

An old rivalry has returned with renewed energy.

Play ball! Whether pitched, caught, kicked, sunk in a basket, or putted into a hole, a ball can provide writers a moving object with which to play. Remember "Casey at the Bat." Play with the exciting, emotional language of a sport of your choice.

Feeling at home in a place you've never been.

Pro tip: Add comfort

Reward yourself while you are writing. (Chew on a toothpick, sip a drink, soak your feet in warm water, etc.)

You have the opportunity to talk with your favorite writer (living or dead).
List your questions.

She found him sitting at the dining room table, head in his hands.

The campers are screaming that there's a monster in the lake. Are you, their counselor, sure they're making it up?

You've discovered that a common food item has miraculous properties heretofore unknown. What food is it? What does it do? Do you share your knowledge?

He held 49 percent of the conglomerate, and she 51 percent. What she announced at the year-end stockholders' meeting astonished him.

Heed what you need and what you read. Indeed, need can lead you to the deed of writing—about a seed or a weed or what you read. Aren't we all agreed that what you read is guaranteed to feed your mind so that you may proceed and succeed? Now, with speed, write about what you read!

You're in a large gift shop in a popular tourist destination, and it's packed with shoppers. In the throng before you, a terrified little girl is crying. You ask her name. She does not understand your language. You pick her up and hoist her above the crowd so she will be seen. What happens next?

Are you calling me a hypochondriac?

Write an alliteration involving clouds.

Waiting in line in the grocery store, you see an elderly lady a few shoppers ahead of you rummage through her purse and drop a $20 bill, unnoticed, to the floor. The person behind her steps on the bill to cover it and looks away, nonchalant. What happens next?

"When I have fears that I may cease to be . . . " (John Keats) Consider the end of life and write how you feel about it.

Pro tip: Who's to say?

Write in first-, second-, or third-person, in your voice or another's. Decide which point of view best suits your purpose.

If there are "Thirteen Ways of Looking at a Blackbird" (Wallace Stevens), there must be at least "Five Ways of Looking at a Sneaker," especially with today's flashy designs.

The vegetables are arguing again.

Write a Crayola poem, connecting the names of the colors to paint a scene. Try spring green, burnt sienna, mahogany, periwinkle, dandelion, and bittersweet.

How did this wind up in court?

A tall tale. Write something that is completely untrue about yourself or someone you know. Be convincing at first, but exaggerate until it is totally outrageous and unbelievable.

At the animal shelter you see your ideal pet. What is it, and why is it the one?

Write a poem about pillows.

The right thing for the wrong reason.

A movie or TV series is being filmed in your neighborhood. What is it? Why is your neighborhood the ideal setting for this story?

Dear Diary . . . today is 9/11/01. Or any memorable date in your life. Chronicle that day.

Do you (or did you) collect things? Stones, frogs in any form, refrigerator magnets? Write about your collection. Why are/were you drawn to these objects?

Your spouse, who has never so much as cooked an egg, gets home a couple of hours before you, secretly having planned to prepare a three-course meal with a fully dressed table. On arrival, you are thrilled. But then . . .

Your son Jack brings home a packet of heirloom seeds from his second grade "Garden Exchange Day." The planted seeds turn out to be uber weeds that grow lusher and healthier with each application of herbicide. What's the story?

You can't make this stuff up. What has happened to you that is so bizarre nobody would believe it?

Find a poem or nursery rhyme written in a foreign language you don't understand. Now compose your own version in English, but without peeking at the translation. Imitate the length, line breaks, and use of long or short words, vowel sounds, alliteration, rhyme, and repetition. Now have fun comparing your poem to the English translation.

Write about a teacher who made you miserable.

Examining the menu, you don't know what to do.

What is it? Sketch—with words—an ordinary object, like an umbrella or an egg, without using the object's name, in a way that someone reading your words knows what you are talking about.

Writing about health problems doesn't have to be heavy, if approached from a lighter side. In "Ode to My Right Knee," Rita Dove begins, "Oh, obstreperous one…" Later, she describes the unpleasant problem, but the outrageous alliteration keeps us amused. "Membranes matter-of-factly / corroding, crazed cartilage calmly chipping / away as another ambulation / begins, bone bruising bone." Write about your "funny bone."

That reflection. In the mirror. That can't be me.

Write a poem in which you compare yourself to an animal. Are you a tall, gawky giraffe? A lumbering bear? A ground-sniffing dachshund? Or are you an eagle, soaring?

At some time or another, we all unwillingly stumble into the country of Pain. Describe what terrain it resembles for you. Desert? Glacier? Swamp? Jungle?

Write a letter to your ten-year-old self, explaining, comforting, encouraging, advising.

Instead of avoiding clichés like the plague, grab one and run away with it.
- Cat got your tongue?
- Fall head over heels
- Laughter is the best medicine
- Waking up on the wrong side of the bed
- Sent a shiver down my spine
- And they all lived happily ever after

Write an over-the-top, no-holds-barred love letter to someone to send or not.

Now write one to yourself.

The last thing I remember . . .

A day in the life of . . . Map your movements. Where do steps/wheels/rails/wings take you? Are you standing or sitting, running or reclining most of the time? Inside or outside? Do you go around the corner or around the country or around the world?

"Looks like Miss Sarah left her bonnet in the wagon. I'll take it on over to her."
"Oh, no, you won't."

Pro tip: Challenge writer's block

When stuck, speak aloud or write a note to the writer's block. This sometimes helps identify the source of the block—critics' voices from the past, lack of confidence, hyper judgmentalism—and helps to gain power over it. While the block's job is to fling down the gauntlet, your job is to use the challenge to get back in the game.

After years of struggles, submissions, and rejections, it's finally happened: A major publisher wants your book and is offering a handsome advance! How do you celebrate?

His yellow legal pad, sharp #8 pencils, and a story in mind. Strong characters, conflicts, locales. "But I need a great beginning," he thought. "And where will it end? Hey, this is a novel. Let it take me wherever it wants to go." He filled a page with an opening idea, some random notes to flesh it out. And then a far-fetched ending:

Taconic Writers was founded in the late 1980s by a few writer friends of New York State's Hudson Valley, who wished to share their work in a supportive environment. Since then, the group has grown to nine members. Although all were "amateurs" at the beginning, the writers have gone on to publish six novels, several children's books, books of nonfiction, and books of poetry, essays, and numerous articles. Taconic Writers also offers public readings and, for nearly two decades, presented an annual program at local libraries. Members enjoy social and literary excursions and continue to meet monthly in one another's homes to share works-in-progress, friendship, and love of the written word.

Elaine Andersen

Cary Phillips Auerbach

Paul Callagy

Jo Hausam

Walter Keady

Ed Lieberthal

Elton Renfroe

Virginia Reynolds

Nannette Stone

Visit us at www.taconicwriters.com